MORE MAD MATH

Compiled and edited
by Jackie Glasthal

SCHOLASTIC INC.
New York Toronto London Auckland Sydney

Illustrated by Holly Kowitt

ISBN 0-590-45259-2

Copyright © 1992 by Scholastic Inc.
All rights reserved. Published by Scholastic Inc.

12 11 10 9 8 7 6 5 4 3 2   2 3 4 5 6/9

Printed in the U.S.A.   28

First Scholastic printing, March 1992

An introduction to . . .

MORE MAD MATH

What do the puzzles in this book have to do with math? EVERYTHING! But that doesn't mean that there's addition, subtraction, multiplication, or division on every page. Mathematicians use lots of other skills, too — like logic and good old common sense. So put your thinking cap on. You'll need it!

Flight Patterns

Ready for your first puzzle adventure? Here's your mission: Help these rockets take off by completing the "countdown" number pattern on each one.

Rockets show these numbers:

A		**B**		**C**		**D**	
	48		160		53		10
	40		80		44		34
	32		40		36		11
	24		20		29		34
	16		10		23		12

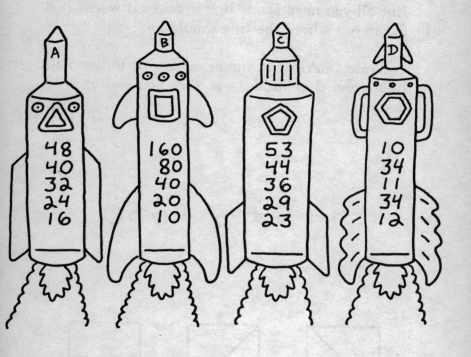

Bonus: See if you can spot the pattern that the rocket windows follow. What would the next rocket window look like?

One-liners

What's wrong with this equation? Everything! But all you need is one line to make it work. Just figure out where the line should go.

While you're at it, figure out a way to lose four lines from this puzzle — so that you end up with just *one*.

$$5 + 5 + 5 = 550$$

Shake On It!

When two people shake hands, there's one hand-shake between them. How many handshakes are there when three people shake hands? Four people? Five people? How many handshakes are there when 15 people shake hands?

Line Designs

You can make beautiful pictures using nothing but these two circles and a few straight lines. Just follow these instructions.

Connect every *fifth* mark on this circle. Don't stop until you get back to your starting point.

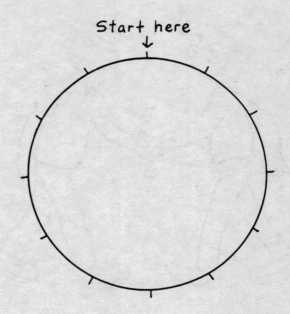

Now connect every *thirteenth* mark on this circle.

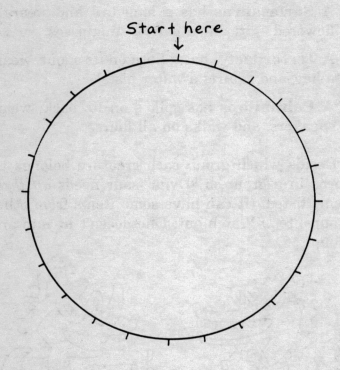

Start here

Sorting "Dyna"-saurs

Check out these "Dyna"-saurs! Can you pick out all three kinds?

- **A Surfasaurus** has a long tail and wears a flowered shirt and a pair of sunglasses.

- **A Terrordactyl** has a horn on its snout, wears a hat, and squirts a water pistol.

- **A Pairahitops** has spikes on its back, wears sneakers, and walks on all fours.

Decide which group each creature belongs to. To be in a group, a "Dyna"-saur needs *all three* items listed. (It can have some items from other groups, too.) Watch out: One doesn't fit into any group!

A

E

Make Room for Logic

Are you a good house detective? Find out! Match each window in the front of this house to the kid that the room belongs to. Write the kid's name in his or her window box.

- Lisa's room is above Julie's.
- Don's room is between Cathy's and Julie's.
- Cathy's room is near the tree.
- Ed's room is closer to Lisa's room than Bill's is.

The Knights of the Round Table

King Arthur has a new law in his kingdom. Here's what it says:

> ## KING'S PROCLAMATION
>
> Three Knights will sit at my next Round Table.
>
> Sir Laughalot will sit between Sir Richard and Sir Henry.
>
> Sir Henry will sit between Sir Boldface and Sir Laughalot.
>
> Sir Boldface will sit between Sir Camelbot and Sir Edgar.
>
> Signed,
> King Arthur

Can you figure out each knight's full name?

Math Search

Circle these math terms in the grid on the next page. (They're printed across, down, backward, and diagonally.) When you're done, write the uncircled letters from left to right in the blank spaces. That will give you the answer to our riddle.

MILLILITER   LENGTH   SUM
CELSIUS   SQUARE   PLUS
CLOCK   INCH   GRAPH
ESTIMATE   HOUR   SUBTRACT
ADD   MILE   DECIMAL
    EQUATION   PROTRACTOR

```
P  S  D  H  P  A  R  G  L  S
R  T  E  C  L  O  C  K  E  U
O  E  C  S  U  M  H  C  N  I
T  T  I  A  S  C  E  O  G  S
R  A  M  N  R  T  I  I  T  L
A  M  A  M  E  T  E  T  H  E
C  I  L  E  A  L  B  D  R  C
T  T  R  U  O  H  I  U  D  S
O  S  Q  U  A  R  E  M  S  A
R  E  T  I  L  I  L  L  I  M
```

RIDDLE: What units do skunks use when they measure?

ANSWER:

_ _ _ _ _ _ _ _ _ _ _

What's for Lunch?

Dare you place an order at the Bad Taste Cafe? These three customers did. Use the waiters' checks and the prices on the next page to figure out what each customer ordered. There are a few possible food combinations to reach the specified totals.

ED'S CHECK	TED'S CHECK	FRED'S CHECK
2 items....$1.55	3 items....$3.05	4 items....$3.25

Spellbound

Here's a way to turn *any* number into a four. Try it!

1. Pick a number ....
2. Spell it out ....
3. Count the letters ....
4. Spell that number of letters out in words ....
5. Keep repeating steps 3 and 4

No matter what number you start with, you'll always end up with the number four!

Flip a Coin!

Have a friend hide a nickel in one hand and a dime in the other. Then tell your friend that you will guess which coin is in each hand. Here's how to do it:

- Have your friend multiply the value of the coin in his or her *right* hand by 4, 6, or 8. Then have your friend multiply the value of the coin in his or her *left* hand by 3, 5, or 7.

- Have your friend add the two numbers together and tell you the total.

- If the total is *even*, the nickel is in your friend's right hand. If it's *odd*, the nickel is in your friend's left hand.

Can you figure out why this trick works?

Make Your Move

Right now this house faces west. But you can make it face east by moving just one line. Go ahead — make your move!

WEST   EAST

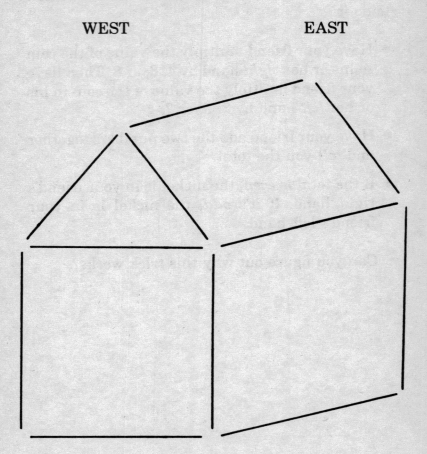

Hats Off to Honest Abe

Abraham Lincoln stood 6 feet, 4 inches tall. That makes him the tallest president the United States has ever had. But when he wore his stovepipe hat, he looked even taller!

Take a good look at the stovepipe hat shown here. Which is longer: the bottom of the hat or its sides?

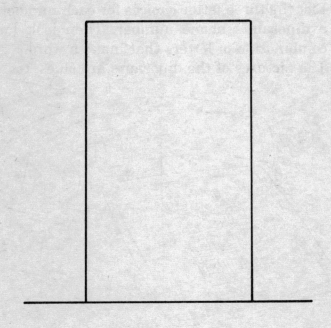

Dial-a-Saurus

Even though it won't do them any good, we came up with perfect phone numbers for these three dinosaurs. Each phone number spells out that dinosaur's nickname — in code! Here's how to decode the nicknames:

- Look at the telephone. On it you'll find the possible letter choices for each number. For example, the number 2 in a phone number could stand for A, B, or C.
- List the three letter choices for each number in a dinosaur's phone number. Then look for a combination of letters that make a word.
- The pictures of the dinosaurs are clues, too.

TRACHODON
244–2455
– – –   – – – –

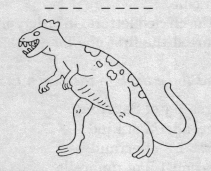

TYRANNOSAURUS REX
843–5464
– – –   – – – –

STEGOSAURUS
729–2225
– – –   – – – –

Funny Fractions

You may not think that fractions are funny. But the fractions on these two pages are good for a laugh or two. Here's how to join in the fun:

- Circle the correct fraction of letters described in each clue.
- Write the circled letters, in order, on the blanks. (We started the first one for you.)

Who had to be back to the beach at midnight?

1. The first 1/4 of Saturday
2. The second 1/2 of kind
3. The first 1/3 of errand
4. The second 1/2 of umbrella

 S __ __ __ __ __ __ __ __ __

What did one copy of this book say to another copy?

1. The first 1/4 of bell
2. The last 2/3 of toy
3. The first 2/5 of dozen
4. The last 2/3 of owe
5. The first 1/2 of hair
6. The first 1/3 of velvet
7. The first 1/2 of probably
8. The middle 1/3 of ill
9. The last 3/4 of gems

___ ___ ___, ___ ___
___ ___ ___ ___ ___ ___
___ ___ ___ ___ ___ ___ ___ ___!

Line Up for Pie!

The Parkers are all ready to pounce on Percy Parker's pizza pie. They don't care what size slices they get. But each Parker wants the same number of pickles, pineapple, and popcorn pieces on his or her slice. They're the best parts of the pie!

To please the Parkers, use three straight lines to cut Percy's pie into five slices. The lines can *intersect* (cut through) one another. But each slice must have the same number of each ingredient on it. (We found two ways to do this puzzle. Can you find them both?)

Candy-Coated Coins

It takes exactly 50 coins to get a yummy $1.00 chocolate bar out of this zany space-aged candy machine. Which 50 coins must you use? (You need at least one quarter, one dime, one nickel, and one penny.)

Keep Counting Sheep
(That's a Hint!)

Farmer Fred is in the market for 100 new animals. He wants to buy cows, sheep, and pigs. And he wants to spend exactly $100 on them — no more, no less. Here are the animals and their prices:

How many of each animal must Farmer Fred buy?

_____ cows   _____ pigs   _____ sheep

Punch It Up!

You'll need a calculator to answer these riddles. Just punch up the answer to each math problem. Then turn the calculator upside down to find out each missing word.

1. 14.816×0.25
   The more you take out of it,
   the bigger it gets.
   It's a _____.

2. $325.677 \div 0.4587$
   It lies under the ground.
   It makes a poor person rich,
   a clean shirt dirty, and
   a cold house warm.
   It's _____.

3. $4687.21 + 45358.13$
   What does Elvis Presley do
   with a blue suede fly swatter?
   _____ _____ away flies!

The Divisibility Bowl

The Delaware Digits are playing the Nevada Numbers in the big end-of-the-year Divisibility Bowl. But all the players' uniforms look the same!

- The numbers on the Delaware Digits' jerseys are divisible by 3. Circle these players.

- The numbers on the Nevada Numbers' jerseys are divisible by 4. Put a box around these players.

- The two referees are wearing jerseys with numbers that are divisible by 5. Put an X through these referees.

So who wins the big game? To find out, add up the numbers on the referees' jerseys. If the sum is divisible by 3, the Delaware Digits win the game. If it's divisible by 4, the Nevada Numbers win.

Canoe Solve These?

1. Riverboat Randee's canoe is 14 inches high. At low tide, 2 inches of it are underwater. During high tide the water level rises 2 feet. How many inches of the canoe are underwater then? ____

2. Randee's canoe can hold up to 300 pounds. And that's exactly how much Randee's pet gorilla Hortense weighs. Randee and her twin sister, Lucy, each weigh 150 pounds. How can the three of them use the canoe to cross the river? (You can bring it back across the river as many times as you like.) _____

_____

Fill 'er Up

Don't try this activity — yet. First picture the problem in your head. Then see if you can pour out the answer without spilling the beans.

1. Fill cup A with beans.
2. Pour half of the beans from cup A into cup B.
3. Pour half of the beans from cup B into cup C.
4. Pour half of the beans from cup A into cup C.
5. Pour all of the beans from cup A into cup D.
6. Pour half of the beans from cup C into cup A.

Which cup contains the most beans now?

Try it and see if you were right!

Sink Your Teeth into This!

Herb the alligator needs help using his new false teeth. The dentist told him to just follow these two rules when he pops them into his mouth:

- Herb must use *all* of the teeth.
- The equation on them must total 100.

"Help me out," says Herb. "Then I can invite you to my swamp for a bite."

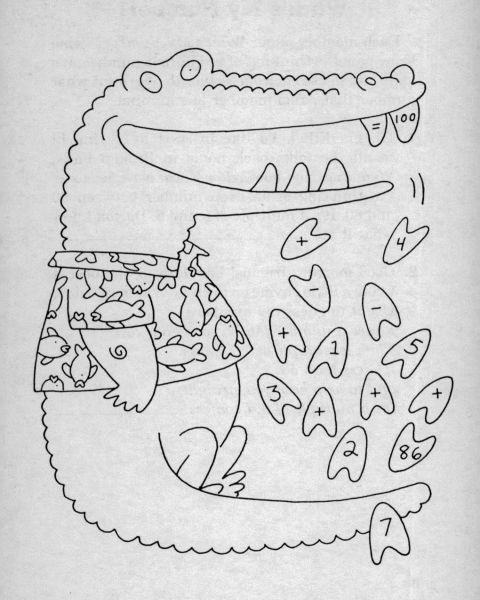

What's My Number?

Each member of our *What's My Number?* game show panel is thinking of a different number. It's up to you to use each one's clues to figure out what number that panel member has in mind.

1. Hi. I'm Ethel. I'd like to start by saying hi to all the folks back home in Broken Falls, Wyoming. Yoo-hoo, *helloooooooo!* Now, let's see. I'm thinking of an even number between 50 and 80. It's a multiple of 5 and 6. Do you know what it is? _____

2. Good morrow, friends! I'm Horatio, the poet. I wrote a little rhyme on my way over here today. Use it to guess my number.
   I have a number that's exactly one less
   Than a multiple of 7, I guess.
   It's less than 58,
   and to help keep you straight,
   It's a multiple of 8, I confess! _____

3. Yee-ha! My name's Mabel. I love bronco-busting, interior decorating — and the number that I'm thinking of. It's an even number somewhere between 5 and 30. Its digits add up to 1. Can you tell me what it is? _____

4. Hi, guys. It's great to be here. I'm Stretch, the tallest short-order cook in Pasta, Pennsylvania. My number is between 2 and 15. It's odd (like my name) and prime (like my steaks). It's a factor of 14 and 28. What is it? _____

Here's a Chilling Riddle:

What happens to people when they're out in the snow too long?

To find the answer:

- Look for each temperature at the bottom of this page on the thermometer. (Be careful: Some of the readings are given in degrees Fahrenheit and some are given in degrees centigrade.)
- Write the letter given on the thermometer in the space above that temperature.

___ ___ ___ ___ ___ ___ ___

45°F 40°C 110°F 70°F   32°F 110°F 45°F

___ ___ ___ ___ ___ ___

25°C 5°C 15°C 90°F 110°F 70°F

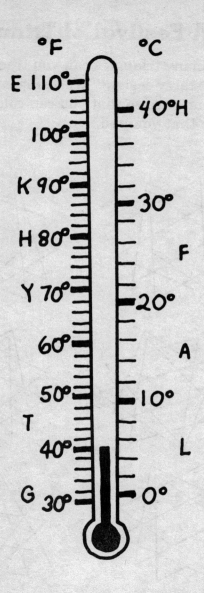

A Festival of Triangles

How many triangles can you track down in one of these starry designs? We've repeated the picture more than once so that you can color in each new triangle that you find.

Weigh to Go!

Poor Priscilla Gorilla has a weight problem. Why? Someone took the weights off her barbell. Now she can't get any exercise!

Priscilla keeps five weights on each side of the barbell. Each side should add up to 100 pounds. Help Priscilla get a grip on her problem. Figure out which weights should go together. It would sure give Priscilla a lift.

Back-and-Forth Numbers

A palindrome is a word or number that reads the same backward and forward. "Madam, I'm Adam" is a palindrome. So is the numer 49,394.

If a number isn't a palindrome, you can usually turn it into one. Start by adding the number to its reverse, like this:

Example: 143

$$
\begin{array}{r}
143 \\
+\,341 \\
\hline
484
\end{array}
$$

484 ←——— a palindrome!

If *that* doesn't work, add the solution to its reverse until you do get a palindrome.

Example: 149

$$
\begin{array}{r}
149 \\
+\,941 \\
\hline
1{,}090
\end{array}
\qquad
\begin{array}{r}
1{,}090 \\
+(0)901 \\
\hline
1{,}991
\end{array}
$$

1,991 ←——— a palindrome!

A Palindrome Puzzle

To complete this puzzle, turn each number clue into a palindrome. (Page 42 shows you how.) Put the palindromes in the grid.

Clues

Across

A. 305
C. 261
E. 26
G. 123
H. 17
J. 4,312
L. 561
N. 40
P. 315
Q. 31
S. 173
T. 94

Down

A. 652
B. 127
D. 4,962
F. 533
G. 13
I. 63,112
K. 420
M. 80
O. 419
R. 331

Downhill Math

Welcome to the *DynaMath* Downhill! It's the toughest ski slope on paper. But you can be an expert on it — even if you've never seen snow.

Just think of a number — any number. Write it in the box at the top. Then do all the math on the hill using scratch paper. Write each answer in the correct box or circle.

How do you know if you're an expert? Look at your answers. Each box should give you the number you started with. If not, check your math. After all, even the best skiers sometimes take a fall!

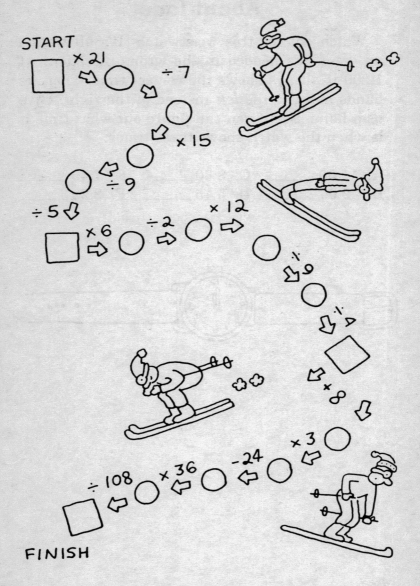

START

☐ ×21 ○ ÷7 ○ ×15 ○ ÷9 ○ ÷5

☐ ×6 ○ ÷2 ○ ×12 ○ ÷9 ○ ÷4 ◇ +8 ○ ×3 ○ −24 ○ ×36 ○ ÷108 ☐

FINISH

About-face

Watch out for this wristwatch. It's all wound up — but it's headed in the wrong direction! At 12:00 it always shows the correct time. Then its hands move to the *left* instead of the right. Give us a hand. See if you can figure out what time it is when the watch shows these times:

A. 11:00 _____ C. 8:30 _____ E. 7:45 _____
B. 9:00 _____ D. 5:15 _____ F. 3:29 _____

The Shadows Know!

This groundhog is in a really deep hole. He has to figure out which one of these three shadows is his. Can you help him out?

Numbers, Please

You may have to look up some of the number facts in this puzzle. But start by plugging in the numbers that you already know. Then solve the problems using the numbers that you write in. Put the answer for clue A in box A, and so on. When you're done with the puzzle, each row, column, and diagonal in the magic square should add up to the number 1,863. Good luck!

Clues

A. ADD: Indianapolis _____ (car race) + the amount of money you get in Monopoly when you pass "GO" _____ + Figure _____ (number shape that ice skaters make).

B. SUBTRACT: First 3 digits in a toll-free phone number _____ − "Slap me _____" (slang expression).

C. MULTIPLY: _____ (one dozen) × number of days in November _____.

D. MULTIPLY: *Snow White and the* _____ *Dwarfs* × 19_____ (the year the movie *The Wizard of Oz* was released).

E. SUBTRACT: Year the pilgrims first celebrated Thanksgiving _____ − number of meters in a kilometer _____.

F. **MULTIPLY AND ADD:** A cat has _____ lives (expression) × number of years in a century _____ + 19_____ (year *Apollo 11* was launched).

G. **MULTIPLY:** San Francisco _____ers (football team) × the age you have to be to vote in the United States _____.

H. **SUBTRACT:** Boeing _____ (one of the biggest passenger airplanes) − number of years celebrated in a tricentennial _____.

I. **SUBTRACT:** Year that is the title of a Prince song _____ − number of minutes in a day _____ − number of cents in a quarter _____.

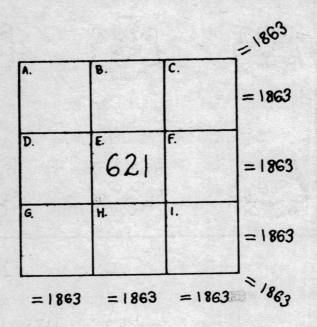

Fence Them In

See if you can give each cat its own cage, just by drawing two squares.

The Bases Are Loaded

Look at the shirts of these baseball players and the coach. The player numbers of any three people in a row (across, down, or diagonally) should add up to 9. Can you figure out what numbers belong on the blank uniforms? The numbers can be whole numbers or decimal numbers.

A Race to the Finish

Use the clues and the logic box below to figure out which racer finished . . .

1st _____ 5th _____
2nd _____ 6th _____
3rd _____ 7th _____
4th _____ 8th _____

We started this logic box for you:

Clues

- Alice finishes next-to-last.
- Mark is not one of the first 4 runners to finish.
- A boy finishes first; Betty or Karrie finish last.
- Tim comes in 5th place; Tom comes in 2nd place.
- One person finishes before Betty and after Tom.

	1st	2nd	3rd	4th	5th	6th	7th	8th
Mark							no	
Betty							no	
Tom							no	
Don							no	
Karrie							no	
Alice	no	no	no	no	no	no	yes	no
Tim							no	
Lisa							no	

Presidential Pets

Believe it or not, some mighty strange pets have lived in the White House at one time or another. Use a logic box and the clues below to figure out which of the four animals shown belonged to each of these presidents:

Abraham Lincoln _____

William Taft _____

Theodore Roosevelt _____

Herbert Hoover _____

Clues

- Hoover's pet doesn't give milk.
- Honest Abe's pet has a beard — just like him!
- Today, toy bears are named after this bear's owner.

To Wrap Things Up . . .

See if you can "unwrap" the two magic squares in this puzzle.

- Find the next number in each pattern in the clues below.
- Write your answer in the correct square.
- When you're done, the sums of numbers in all the rows, columns, and diagonals on each side of the box should be the same.

Clues

Front of Box
A. 6, 12, 18, _____
B. 12, 15, 13, 16, 14, _____
C. 66, 55, 44, 33, _____
D. 9, 9, 9, 19, 19, 19, 9, 9, 9, _____
E. 56, 49, 42, 35, 28, _____
F. 67, 56, 45, 34, _____
G. 16, 7, 17, 8, 18, 9, 19, 10, _____
H. 125, 100, 75, 50, _____
I. 3, 4, 6, 9, 13, _____

Side of Box

J. 10, 20, 30, _____

K. 27, 26, 29, 28, 31, 30, _____

L. 38, 39, 49, 38, 38, 39, 39, _____

M. 55, 50, 45, 40, _____

N. 17, 19, 23, 29, _____

O. 30, 36, 31, 38, 34, 42, _____

P. 6, 12, 18, 24, 30, _____

Q. 26, 27, 29, 32, 36, _____

R. 544, 272, 136, 68, _____

Answers

Pages 4-5 *Flight Patterns*

Here is the next number in each rocket's countdown pattern:
A. 8 (Subtract 8 from each number.)
B. 5 (Divide each number by 2.)
C. 18 (Subtract 1 less than the time before.)
D. 34 (Every other number increases by 1. The other number is always 34.)

BONUS: Each rocket window is in a shape with one more side than the one before it. The next rocket would have a window with 7 sides.

Page 6 *One-liners*

Turn either plus sign into a 4 and the equation works!

Here's what the puzzle looks like after you remove the four lines:

Page 7 *Shake On It!*

When three people shake hands there are 3 (2 + 1) handshakes.
When four people shake hands there are 6 (3 + 2 + 1) handshakes.
When five people shake hands there are 10 (4 + 3 + 2 + 1) handshakes.
When 15 people shake hands there are 105 (14 + 13 + 12 + 11 + 10 + 9 + 8 + 7 + 6 + 5 + 4 + 3 + 2 + 1) handshakes!

Pages 8–9 *Line Designs*

Here are what the two line designs will look like:

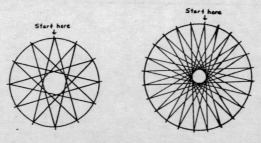

Pages 10–11 *Sorting "Dyna"-saurs*

Surfasaurus — A; Terrordactyl — C, E; Pairahitops — B, F.

Page 12 *Make Room for Logic*

Here's how the house should look:

Page 13 *The Knights of the Round Table*

The knights' full names are Sir Edgar Laughalot, Sir Henry Camelbot, and Sir Richard Boldface.

Pages 14–15 *Math Search*

The answer to the riddle is SCENTIMETERS.

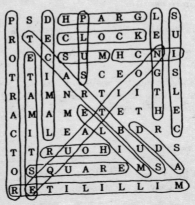

Pages 16–17 *What's for Lunch?*

Ed ordered Shoestring Potatoes and either Fish 'n Sticks or Split Pea Pudding.

Ted ordered Shoestring Potatoes, a Gumball Float, and a Sand Sandwich.

Fred ordered Shoestring Potatoes, a Gumball Float, Squashed Squash, and Tuna Surprise.

Page 19 *Flip a Coin!*

If the nickel is in your friend's left hand the sum of the digits will be odd because you're multiplying five cents by an odd number.

Page 20 *Make Your Move*

The line to be moved is circled on Figure A. Figure B shows what the house will look like once you move that line.

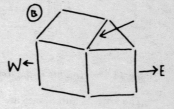

Page 21 *Hats Off to Honest Abe*

The bottom and sides of the hat are the same length.

Pages 22–23 *Dial-a-Saurus*

The Trachodon's phone number spells out BIG BILL.

The Tyrannosaurus Rex's phone number spells out THE KING.

The Stegosaurus's phone number spells out SAW BACK.

Pages 24–25 *Funny Fractions*

SANDERELLA had to be back to the beach at midnight.

One copy of this book says to the other: BOY, DO WE HAVE PROBLEMS!

Page 26 *Line Up for Pie!*

Here are the two ways that we found to divide the pie:

Page 27 *Candy-Coated Coins*

To get a candy bar out of the machine you need 45 pennies, 2 nickels, 2 dimes, and 1 quarter.

Page 28 *Keep Counting Sheep (That's a Hint!)*

Farmer Fred must buy 5 cows, 1 pig, and 94 sheep.

Page 29 *Punch It Up!*

1. HOLE
2. OIL
3. HE SHOOS

Pages 30–31 *The Divisibility Bowl*

These players are on the Delaware Digits: 63, 3,219, 7,203, 5,001, 402.
These players are on the Nevada Numbers: 3,736, 8,888, 6,908, 728, 572.
These players are referees: 370 and 125.
That means that the Delaware Digits win the game.

Page 32 *Canoe Solve These?*

1. As the water level rises, so does the canoe. It will still be 2 inches below the surface of the water!
2. First Randee and Lucy should take the canoe across the river. Then one of them should bring the canoe back to the gorilla. After the gorilla has crossed the river by itself, the sister who has already crossed the river can go back across and get her sister.

Page 33 *Fill 'er Up*

All four cups will contain 1/4 cup of beans.

Pages 34–35 *Sink Your Teeth into This!*

Herb has to add together all of the numbers on the teeth except for 3 and 1, which he should subtract. The order of operations doesn't matter.

Page 36–37 *What's My Number?*

1. Ethel's number is 60.
2. Horatio's number is 48.
3. Mabel's number is 10.
4. Stretch's number is 7.

Pages 38–39 *Here's a Chilling Riddle:*

The answer to the riddle is THEY GET FLAKEY.

Page 40 *A Festival of Triangles*

We counted 34 triangles in the design.

Page 41 *Weigh to Go!*

These weights should go together: 8, 10, 14, 22, and 46. The remaining weights, 5, 12, 21, 28, and 34 should also go together.

Page 43 *A Palindrome Puzzle*

Here's the completed grid:

A8	0	B8			C7	D4	7
8		4				6	
8		E8	F8		G4	4	4
H8	I8		J6	K4	4	6	
		L4	M8	8	4		N4	O4
P8	2	8		Q4	R4		6
	4				6		6
S9	8	9			T4	8	4

Pages 44–45 *Downhill Math*

There is no one correct answer.

Page 46 *About-face*

Here are the times:

A. 1:00   C. 3:30   E. 4:15
B. 3:00   D. 6:45   F. 8:31

Page 47 *The Shadows Know!*

The shadow on your left is the correct shadow.

Pages 48–49 *Numbers, Please*

Here is the completed magic square:

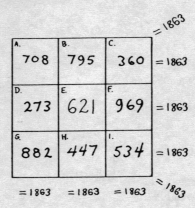

Page 50 *Fence Them In*

Here's how the completed puzzle will look:

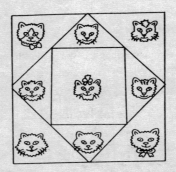

Page 51 *The Bases Are Loaded*

Here is how the baseball diamond looks when the blank uniforms are numbered:

Page 52 *A Race to the Finish*

Here is the order of winners:

1st: Don
2nd: Tom
3rd: Lisa
4th: Betty

5th: Tim
6th: Mark
7th: Alice
8th: Karrie

Page 53 *Presidential Pets*

Abraham Lincoln owned the goat.
William Taft owned the cow.
Theodore Roosevelt owned the bear.
Herbert Hoover owned the alligator.

Pages 54–55 *To Wrap Things Up . . .*

Here's what the completed magic squares look like:

Acknowledgments

Lots of people contributed to the puzzles that went into this book. I owe special thanks to these grown-ups . . .

Daniel Bar-Zeev
Lisa Basani
Richard Bollinger
Carolyn Brunetto
David Brunetto
Aileen Chang
Deanna Cook
Joe D'Agnese
Gary Drevitch

Steve Foster
Lou Glasthal
Rachel Maizes
Barbara Nehmad
Tracey Randinelli
Josh Rapps
Jill Safro
David Schaffer
Jack Silbert

. . . and these kids:

Sheila Akbar
Dan Beel
Adam Benveniste
Caren Benveniste
Meghan Conway
Jim Cotter
Caitlin Darcy
Angie Fredrickson
Jana Geiger
Emily Halpern
Rachel Kauffman
Hilary Kelly
Elena Kim

Meghan Lattimore
Einat Levy
Tim Oleson
Mandy Schneider
Brian Sesterhenn
Elizabeth Steinhoff
Sergio Tortin
Bic Tram
Jennifer Wallace
Catherine Weidinger
Julia Wolters
Sarah Wuestefeld